W9-CSY-209

Laura Lee Gulledge

AMULET BOOKS, NEW YORK

Sparks

There are three things I think you should know about me.

One: I make lamps. I've been making them since my grandfather taught me the basics when I was a kid.

Two: I like old things. I might be just 17, but I have an old-fashioned soul.

Sometimes I feel like I was born in the wrong time.

Good *yaaawn* morning, Will!

But I still have my Aunt Elsie. Elsie is also an old family name. She goes by Ella.

There are three things you should know about Ella Foxx...

One: She runs the family business next door. Foxxden Antiques.

TINDERBOX

KISS THE LIBRARI

Two: She's just... rad. I don't use that adjective often, but Ella's quietly badass.

Bright Ideas

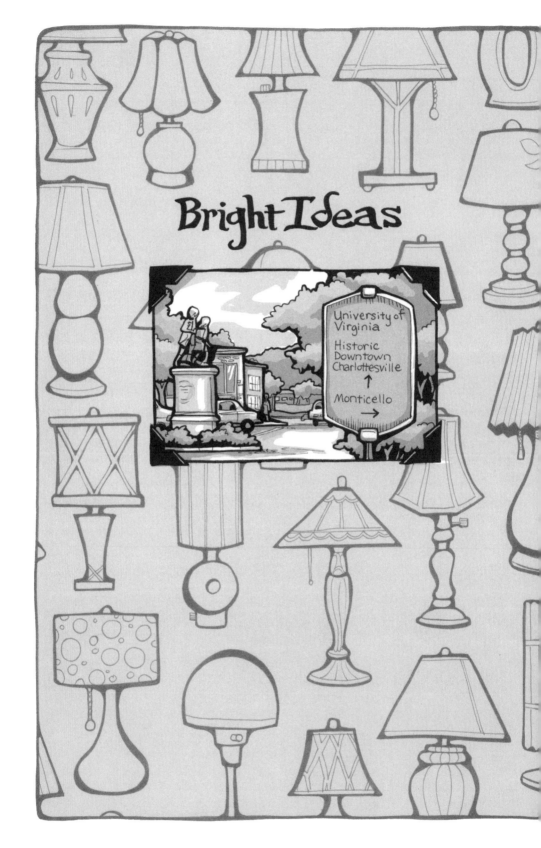

University of
Virginia

Historic
Downtown
Charlottesville
↑

Monticello
→

Shedding Light

At least they bought stuff.

Wow, that nickname was a blast from the past.

Makes me think of Penny. Your mom sure couldn't resist silly nicknames, right?

Well, anyway...That guy sure had a good memory.

Foreshadowing

You'll figure it out. You always do.

And if you can't, you can always live in cardboard box with me after graduation.

Oh no!

Oh what?!

This cookie's ruined! Someone licked it.

How tragic! Guess I'll just have to dispose of it for you.

Sheesh... girls.

Well, you know me...

"I love old things. They make me feel sad."

"...It's happy for deep people."*

*Sally Sparrow, "Doctor Who."

But you can volunteer if you like. Just talk to Desmond.

ADAM! We're not hanging those yet! Did you even READ the schedule?!

Shees Someo has to w the pa aroun here

Don't mind Ava. She's just territorial. She doesn't like other girls.

And you like ther TOO muc

I thought you'd like this place. Lots of ghosts.

You're right, it is quite up my alley!

That was great! Thanks for dragging me down here.

Lamps are "functional"? Heh. Who cares what HE thinks...

What was that, Will?

Oh, nothin. Just thinki about, uh, t Blake guy

Ahh... Blake. He has the most amazing blue eyes. And he's so poetic.

He's definitely got a silver tongue.

It's probably for the best that I can't perform.

I'd just embarrass myself anyway.

OutWhitted

uh-oh.

Well, Emmett's in the tub.

It's official, then: Whitney approaches!

Okay?

Okaaay.

Don't b
yourself
Someti
I think
forge

...we're
foxxes.

foxxes!

Will-Powered

Shadowboxing

Illuminated

Huh, that's strange...

The stoplight over there.

It's green. So what?

It's GRE

The power is back! And the villagers rejoice!!

The reign of whitney finally over About frigg time.

Epilogue

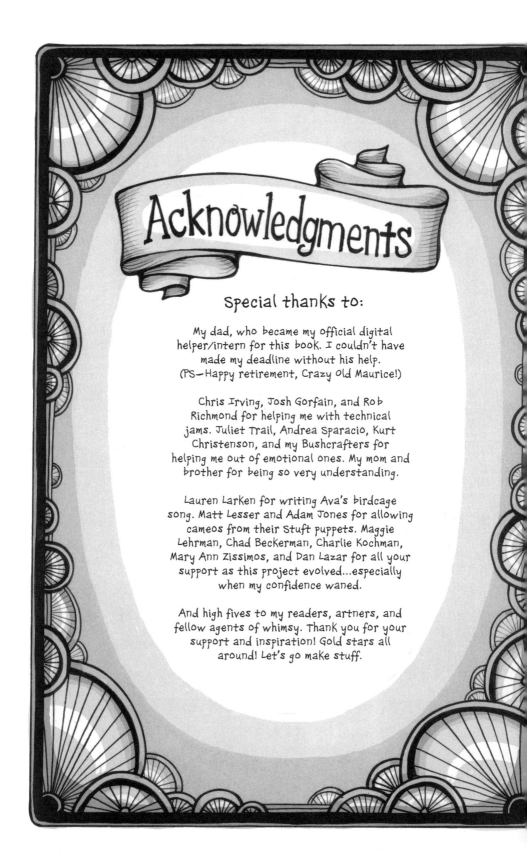

Acknowledgments

Special thanks to:

My dad, who became my official digital helper/intern for this book. I couldn't have made my deadline without his help. (PS—Happy retirement, Crazy Old Maurice!)

Chris Irving, Josh Gorfain, and Rob Richmond for helping me with technical jams. Juliet Trail, Andrea Sparacio, Kurt Christenson, and my Bushcrafters for helping me out of emotional ones. My mom and brother for being so very understanding.

Lauren Larken for writing Ava's birdcage song. Matt Lesser and Adam Jones for allowing cameos from their Stuft puppets. Maggie Lehrman, Chad Beckerman, Charlie Kochman, Mary Ann Zissimos, and Dan Lazar for all your support as this project evolved...especially when my confidence waned.

And high fives to my readers, artners, and fellow agents of whimsy. Thank you for your support and inspiration! Gold stars all around! Let's go make stuff.

Will & Whit

Inspiration Board

Wilhelmina

Wilhelmina "Willa" Maer Lansford, [?]
1905

Elsie

The first spark of inspiration for Will was this photo of my great-grandmother. She had this spirit to her that captivated me. I've always felt a connection with the "stong-willed" women in the family tree. Ella stemmed from my other great-grandmother, who played piano for silent movies.

Elsie Huckstep
Bowling Green, MO
1915

wristwatch that has a light inside

single bulb or wrapped in xmas lights

hoopskirt chandelier

I first got to know Will through designing fifty lamps I thought she'd make.

Parasol chandeliers

curtain of bulbs hanging around her desk

first character sketch

Willy

Isabel

The carnival was rooted in my love of creating art installations, whimsical sets, and interactive events.

And this is my drawing of Hurricane Isabel (2003), my original inspiration for Whitney. However, Hurricane Sandy arrived as I was drawing the storm, so she deserves some credit, too.

me

Cut Out Page

But only cut if this is YOUR book!

Blue Crush Cookies

Anyone can use food coloring to dye a cookie blue. But if you're anything like Noel, you're willing to put in a little extra effort for someone you're sweet on. So our Blue Crush Cookies are colored naturally! Thank you, Paige and Anton Mikuriya, for bringing this recipe to life. Enjoy!

-INGREDIENTS-

*1 cup fresh blueberries, washed
*1 cup water

*1/2 cup sugar. White is ideal for color intensity
*Your favorite chocolate chip cookie recipe & ingredients

-DIRECTIONS-

*Step 1. Prepare your chocolate chip cookie recipe to the point where you'd add the chocolate chips.

*Step 2. Now for the blue part: Place the blueberries, water, and sugar in a small pot. Cook for 30 minutes on mid to low heat, stirring occasionally, and covered with a lid. You can use more or less sugar depending on the sweetness of your particular berries...and how strong your sweet tooth is.

*Step 3. Using a slotted spoon, remove the cooked berries and gently HAND MIX the blueberries into your cookie dough along with your chocolate chips. It's normal for the batter to look grey at this point, so don't fret.

*Step 4. And now bake 'em like usual, and behold as they turn blue! I personally like to sprinkle a little sea salt on top as a finishing touch, but feel free to come up with your own variation.

Artistic License

You ↗

May you always fail big, speak truths, and imagine the impossible.
Your new Artner, Laura Lee

Signature   Date

FUN Permission Slip

_____ (your name) hereby gives permission for myself to play, dream, explore, and try new things free from apology or fear of judgment.

_____ Signature
_____ Date

Write your own FORTUNE

Pssst.... This part of the paper has special powers. Write your desired fortune (like from a fortune cookie) on one of the slips and carry it in your pencil case or wallet. And wait...

About the Author

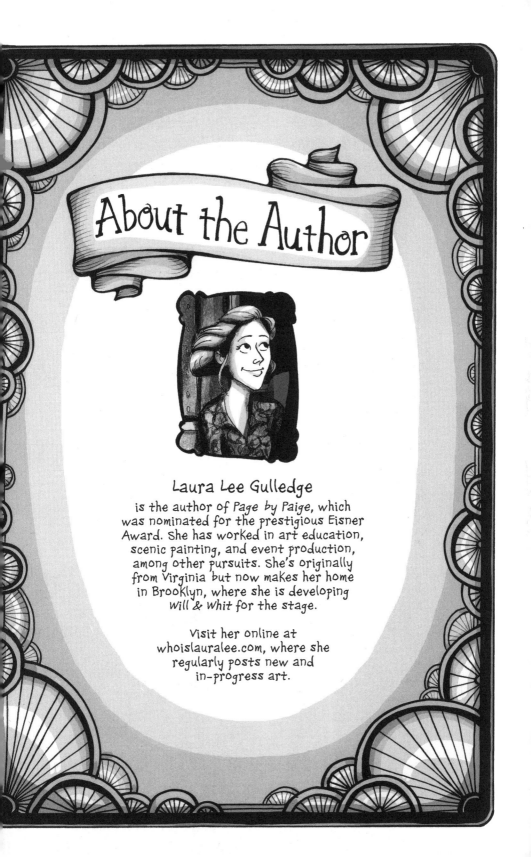

Laura Lee Gulledge

is the author of *Page by Paige*, which was nominated for the prestigious Eisner Award. She has worked in art education, scenic painting, and event production, among other pursuits. She's originally from Virginia but now makes her home in Brooklyn, where she is developing *Will & Whit* for the stage.

Visit her online at whoislauralee.com, where she regularly posts new and in-progress art.

To COM from LLG

Library of Congress Control Number: 2012955192

ISBN: 978-1-4197-0546-5

Text and illustrations copyright © 2013 Laura Lee Gulledge
Book design by Laura Lee Gulledge and Chad W. Beckerman

Printed and bound in U.S.A
10 9 8 7 6 5 4 3 2 1

ABRAMS
THE ART OF BOOKS SINCE 1949
115 West 18th Street
New York, NY 10011
www.amuletbooks.com